THE LITERATE GARDENER'S NOTEBOOK

THE LITERATE
GARDENER'S
NOTEBOOK

FROM THE WRITINGS OF
LOUISE BEEBE WILDER
AND OTHERS

Illustrations by
SIA KASKAMANIDIS

Hartley & Marks
PUBLISHERS

Published by
HARTLEY & MARKS PUBLISHERS INC.
P. O. Box 147   3661 West Broadway
Point Roberts, WA   Vancouver, BC
98281   V6R 2B8

ISBN 0-88179-138-5 (notebook)

Design and composition by The Typeworks
Set in CENTAUR

Printed in the U.S.A.

Introduction

THERE ARE MANY gates into the world of reality and gardening is one of them. As we dig and plant we sweat and strain our backs and get deliciously tired and when we go to bed we sleep so soundly that we do not hear the rain pattering on the roof, but upon awakening in the morning, with our first conscious breath we smell the sweet, clean air, and when we hurry down into the garden, all sunny and dewy it gives us a real thrill to see each little plant, still carrying raindrops in its leaves, standing up straight and strong, having imbibed nourishment from the moist earth we had enriched, made porous and crumbly for them.

Although most amateur gardeners begin tentatively and with gloves on it is pleasant to see how they slowly change until the love for growing plants and arranging them artistically takes complete possession of them and the whole world is colored over with the hue of their hobby. Although they do not go into gardening with the object of improving themselves, yet shy people become friendly and stiff ones thaw out, and the most unsuspected talents for combining colors both indoors and out are manifested, as is the ability for making and recording scientific observations. The further one goes along the road the more branches and related subjects one finds opening off from it and one has no idea whither these little side paths are going to lead. One thing is certain, however, that the people one meets as one travels along the garden path are delightful, remarkably generous and invariably genuine. Their eyes are bright, their faces bronzed, their hands are full of callouses, and their hearts are brimming over with the love of plants.

HELEN MORGENTHAU FOX
July, 1932, from *The Fragrant Path* by
LOUISE BEEBE WILDER

Louise Beebe Wilder

By the time of her death in 1938, Louise Beebe Wilder had developed a reputation as one of America's finest gardening writers. This reputation rested partly on the nine books she published on different aspects of gardening in North America and partly on the monthly columns she wrote for the magazine *American Gardening*. Through her books and articles, Mrs. Wilder cultivated not just an audience for her thoughts on gardening but also a genuine dialogue with her readers, one that she credited with broadening her knowledge and fueling her inspiration.

Reputations and books are both fragile things. That Louise Wilder's reputation continues to flourish and her books to be reprinted are tributes to the depth of her knowledge and the elegance of her prose. Her knowledge was the real thing, based on her experiences in her own gardens and spiced, as it is for most passionate lovers, by equal parts appreciation and exasperation. Plants did not always do what she asked of them, and Mrs. Wilder often conceded that a flower's willfulness is a large part of its charm.

Her prose survives and continues to seduce new readers because it is suffused with wit in the old sense of the term. Mrs. Wilder esteemed and often quoted from the English gardening writers of the seventeenth century. Her dialogue with Bacon, Parkinson, Rea, and Gerard was no less spirited and fruitful than the one she cultivated with her contemporaries. For those earlier writers, "wit" was not restricted in its meaning to a sense of humor (although Mrs. Wilder had that in superabundance); instead it referred to a person's native genius, to the imaginative power of the mind. It is this liveliness of thought, this persistent ability to surprise and delight, that animates Mrs. Wilder's books and puts her readers in the proper frame of mind to see, with Blake, "a heaven in a wild flower."

Allen Lacy, himself no mean practitioner of the art, once summarized Mrs. Wilder's contribution to the tradition of crafting fine English prose on the subject of gardens. "Among distinguished company," he said, "she was clearly a luminary."

ED O'CONNOR
February, 1997

January

AND THEN THERE comes one day the peculiar sharp and penetrating fragrance of new fallen snow, the purest and most innocent of all scents, yet perhaps the most exciting. It fills the world and seems to penetrate our apathy, inciting us to work hard and to play hard until again creep into our consciousness those first disturbing aromas of a new order, those delicate airs that presage the coming of spring, that no barriers of brick or stone can keep out, no city stenches disguise, because they are generated in great part within ourselves.

> January dawn
> The snow still lies upon the ground,
> And yet I feel
> The shadow of the scent of flowers;
> Breathless the firs against the gray—
> So still the air
> That hung upon a bare rose spray
> Are drops of rain
> Left there by midnight showers—
>   . . .
> Black head atilt
> A chickadee
> Whistles the first love-notes of the year.

1

2

3

4

5

*A garden full of sweet odours is
a garden full of charm.*

—L.B.W.

6

7

8

9

10

11

12

13

14

15

16

Smell is the most memoristic of the senses.

—E.F. BENSON

17

18

19

20

21

22

23

24

25

26

*Fragrance speaks to many to whom
colour and form say little, and it "can
bring as irresistibly as music emotions
of all sorts to mind."*

—L.B.W.

27

28

29

30

31

February

WHAT DAVID GRAYSON calls a downright good nose is a blessing to its possessor at all seasons in a garden, but never more so than in the spring. If our sense of smell is sluggish spring will lag for us until the strong scented flowers of May and June force themselves into our consciousness, and we shall have missed more than half the ecstasy. We shall have missed, for instance, that winter day in January, or February, when we step out of the door and suddenly smell the spring. In all external things it is still winter, snow lies about us, the air is cruelly sharp; but something new has crept into the world over night and the nose detects it. It is the best scent of the year. All sweet things seem to be in it, all things young and fresh and uncloying.

1

2

3

4

5

6

7

8

9

10

No other in the five senses is more subtle
in its suggestion than the sense of smell or
more unmistakably reminiscent of a time
and state in which one was something else
and possibly something better.

—SOMERS

11

12

13 6 — 9:00

14

15 5:45 — 10:30

16   6:30 — 10:00

17

18

19

20

Gardens are sweetest when the air is
mild and full of moisture.

—L.B.W.

March

ANNUALS LABOUR under the disadvantage of being annuals. They blossom, seed and die and next year we must begin all over again with them. But if they are fragrant they amply pay their way and the trouble we are put to in their behalf seems as nothing in comparison with the pleasure we have derived from them. Annual flowers with a sweet scent are not so many but that most of them might be included in a fair sized garden; some of them are indispensable to any garden. Who would be without the spicy scent of stocks, of mignonette, or the cool sweetness of the sweet pea?

1

2

3

4

5

In mediaeval times there was a widespread belief in the efficacy of flowers and leaf scents as cures or alleviations for all sorts of ills of the flesh, but more especially of the spirit.

—L.B.W.

April

11

12

13

14

15

16

17

18

19

20

How often the scent of some flower —
honeysuckle, jasmine, lilac — stealing
upon our senses in the night, causes
darkness to flower in visions of
hallucinatory vividness.

—L.B.W.

April

21

22

23

24

25

26

27

28

29

Nor is the fragrant garden ever wholly
our own. Over hedge or wall, and often
far down the highway, it sends a
greeting, . . . And who shall say that the
gentle sweet airs for a moment enveloping
them do not send each on his way touched
in some manner, cheered, softened, filled
with hope or renewed vigour, arrested,
perhaps in some devious course?

—L.B.W.

30

May

"AN AMERICAN SPRING," wrote Charles Downing, father of landscape gardening in America, "may be said fairly to begin with the blossoming of the apricot and the elm tree, and with the ripening of the first strawberries." The strawberry is the harbinger among the fruits; the earnest of good things to follow, and its delicate scented freshness, pungent and penetrating, is one of the delights of the oncoming season. Thoreau frequently marked the similarity of the earth's fragrance to strawberries and wrote in his journal, June 9, 1853, "It is natural that the first fruit which the earth bears should emit, and be, as it were, an embodiment of that vernal fragrance with which the air has teemed. Strawberries are its manna, found ere long where that fragrance has filled the air." "Is there anything like the odour of Strawberries?" wrote John Burroughs. "The next thing to tasting them is to smell them."

1

2

3

4

5

*It is now the time of Laylock, White
Thorn, Musk, Florence Iris, Lady's
Smock and White Violets.*

—J.R. ANDERSON

6

7

8

9

10

11

12

13

14

15

Which May had painted with his softe
*   showers*
This garden full of leaves and of flowers.
*   —CHAUCER*

16

17

18

19

20

21

22

23

24

25

A nosegay of sweet scented flowers is always an acceptable gift to visiting friends, especially if they hail from the city.

—L.B.W.

26

27

28

29

30

31

June

THE BOUQUET OF the garden on a June day is rich and heterogeneous. Turn this way and that and the nose is accosted by wave after wave of sweetness from rose, iris, honeysuckle, mock orange, peony, pink, and besides these chief distillers, any one of which we should count as good for a month's allowance of perfume, there are many lesser alembics at work transmuting their juices into enchanting airs.

Peonies, that are among the oldest flowers we grow in the garden, play a significant part in the *omnium gatherum* of June odours. At their best they may be said to have a coarse rose scent. In it is much of the sweetness and transparency of rose perfume, much of its refreshing quality, but back of this is something indefinable that is a little rank, a suggestion of something medicinal perhaps, which however seldom reaches a point, though it varies in strength in the different varieties, of being actively unpleasant. This curious sub-odour, so to speak, is most marked in the single and semi-double varieties, and it is said to be due to the strong, rather rank odour of the pollen that predominates over what little scent the petals may possess.

June

1

2

3

4

5

6

7

8

9

10

What cordials make this curious broth,
This broth of smells that feeds and
fats my mind?

—G. HERBERT

11

12

13

14

15

16

17

18

19

20

Fragrance, perhaps, speaks more clearly, however, to age than to youth. With the young it may not pass much beyond the olfactory nerve, but with those who have started down the far side of the hill it reaches into the heart.

—L.B.W.

21

22

23

24

25

26

27

28

29

30

Here, in this sequestered close,
Bloom the hyacinth and rose;
Here beside the modest stock
Flaunts the flaring hollyhock;
Here without a pang, one sees
Ranks, conditions, and degrees.

—A. DOBSON

July

AS THE SUMMER with its increasing light and heat advances fewer perfumes of definite character are noted, but the sultry air is burdened with an agreeable soft medley of odours sweeping in from the hayfields, from the plantations of resinous evergreens and from many kinds of flowers. Aside from the heavy lily scents and some of the elaborate exhalations of the night-blooming annuals, perhaps the most individual odours of the summer garden are derived from certain plants which persons of hyper-sensitive nasal organs may turn from in disgust. I call these plants Nose-twisters, because the rough and heady scent of nasturtium, which seems to have in it something bitter, something peppery, and a vague underlying smoky sweetness, is representative of them, and the name nasturtium, an old Latin word used by Pliny, was derived by him from narsus, the nose, and tortus, twisted, in reference to the supposed contortions of the nose caused by the hot pungent odour and taste of these flowers. Personally I am very fond of the odour of the Nose-twisters, marigold, calendula, chrysanthemum, tansy, and others of a like bitter pungence, and find it always invigorating and refreshing. Possibly this taste is inherited for I am told that my Virginian great-grandfather was very partial to it and always insisted upon having a bowl of marigolds at his elbow when they were in season while he wrote his sermons, saying that to smell them cleared his brain. Even to look at marigolds we are told in some old books (and we can well believe it) serves to draw ill-humours from the head.

1

2

3

4

5

The yellowed pages of ancient works on
gardening seem to give off the scents of the
beloved old favorites — gilliflower, stock,
sweet rocket, wall flower, white violet.

—L.B.W.

6

7

8

9

10

11

12

13

14

15

When I pick or crush in my hand a twig of bay, or brush against a bunch of rosemary, or tread upon a tuft of thyme, or pass through incense-laden Cistus, I feel that here is all that is best and purest and most refined, and nearest to poetry in the range of faculty of the sense of smell.

—G. JEKYLL

July

16

17

18

19

20

21

22

23

24

25

26

The gardens of my youth were fragrant
gardens and it is their sweetness rather
than their patterns or their furnishings
that I now most clearly recall.

—L.B.W.

27

28

29

30

31

August

IF IT COMES TO choosing between a climber with fragrant flowers and one that appeals only to the eye it would seem the simple part of wisdom to select one that yields a profit both to the sight and to the sense of smell. "A rose looking in at the window" is always a delight but if it be a sweet scented rose so much the more delightful. To veil our outdoor retreats with fragrant climbers, or to twine them about doors and windows, so that their sweet airs are carried into the rooms upon the wings of every breeze, is to thread our days with a subtle, gentle happiness, a happiness indefinable but profoundly felt. To sleep in a room beyond whose casement honeysuckle scrambles and to awake in the night to the exquisite fragrance that inspires the darkness is an experience of rare quality. Such things invade life's commonplace routine with an ecstatic pleasure.

1

2

3

4

5

6

7

8

9

10

Awake, O north wind, and come, thou south; blow upon my garden that the spices may flow forth.

—CANT. IV. 16

11

12

13

14

15

16

17

18

19

20

We have juggled the sweet pea into the last word in hues and furbelows, and all but lost its sweetness; we have been careless of the rose's scent, and have made of the wistful mignonette a stolid and indecorous wedge of vulgarity.

—L.B.W.

21

22

23

24

25

26

27

28

29

30

31

*Man only doth smel and take delight
in the odours of flowers and sweet
things.*

—W. BULLEIN

September

OFTEN I HAVE followed a scent up the breeze on a sharp autumn day to find at the end of the quest a witch hazel thicket, or even a single tree, in its quaint regalia. When you draw near and thrust your nose among the blossoms you perceive little or no perfume unless you crush them, but withdraw and go about other affairs and the sweetest airs will overtake and envelop you. Sitting one Indian Summer's day this autumn in the lovely garden of Rollo Peters with several members of that delightful South Mountain group of craftsmen, we suddenly became aware of a distinct but intermittent fragrance. All about us were the amber and russet tags of the spent summer, no flower was in sight. We were curious and looked about and presently we saw bending over the near-by brook a crooked witch hazel in full flower. The fantastic little tree was sending us messages, remaining quiet for a time and then again seeking to get in touch with us. When we came close to it, it withheld its sweetness.

1

2

3

4

5

For the most part fragrant flowers are light in colour or white.

—L.B.W.

September

6

7

8

9

10

11

12

13

14

15

The gift of perfume to a flower is a
special grace like genius or like beauty,
and never becomes common or cheap.

—J. BURROUGHS

16

17

18

19

20

21

22

23

24

25

*The perfume of the plant is not
always found in its flower. Sometimes
it is in the root, sometimes in the seeds,
the bark, the gum or oils, often in the
leaves and stalks.*

—L.B.W.

26

27

28

29

30

October

AFTER THE FIRST frosts many odours are released to the world. From the herb garden especially comes a rich melange of scents; heliotrope is penetrating in its sweetness after a first nipping; from the roadside where wild grapes still hang comes a winy aroma, and from dying fern fronds that curiously heady odour of earth and herbage which is especially theirs. Our sense of smell seems to become keener with the sharpness in the air and we note the fragrance of the pine, the sweet resinous tang of the red cedar, and better still that of the savin juniper, which has a rich underlying bitterness that is most invigorating. And on the warm side of the arbor vitae hedge we catch a scent of ripe strawberries, and note that the scent of the Douglas fir is good close at hand and is also carried to a considerable distance.

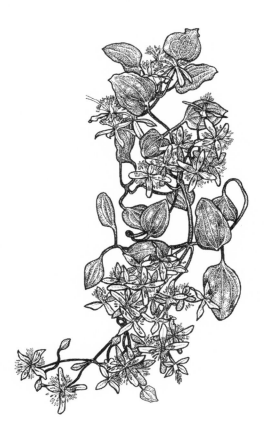

1

2

3

4

5

6

7

8

9

10

*Nature imitates all things in flower.
They are at once the most beautiful
and the ugliest objects, the most
fragrant and the most offensive to the
nostrils.*

—H.D. THOREAU

11

12

13

14

15

16

17

18

19

20

*For it is a great pleasure to identify a
friendly odour in the fields.*

—D. GRAYSON

21

22

23

24

25

26

27

28

29

30

The loveliest flowers the closest cling to earth.

—J. KEBLE

31

November

THERE ARE SCENTS abroad in the still autumn days whose composition it is impossible to analyze. Go out of doors on a dull November day and sniff the breeze. Brown leaves lie all about you, the garden beds are almost bare, yet the air is full of strange perfumes, stimulating and full of vitality. The tang of bitter-sweet chrysanthemums is there, the acrid fumes of wood smoke, the rich pungence of trodden walnut leaves, and now and then one catches a whiff of pure spring, perhaps caught by the breeze from the thready blossoms of the witch hazel that "by their color as well as fragrance belong to the saffron dawn of the year, suggesting amid all the signs of autumn, falling leaves and frost, that the life of nature, by which she eternally flourishes, is untouched."

1

2

3

4

5

*Especially should small gardens,
I think, be full of sweet scented
flowers; it gives them a loveable,
intimate quality.*

—L.B.W.

6

7

8

9

10

11

12

13

14

15

Trailing odorous plants which curtain
out the day with loveliest flowers.
—SHELLEY

16

17

18

19

20

21

22

23

24

25

*And how good the earth smells when
we first go questing about and poking
among the leaves.*

—L.B.W.

26

27

28

29

30

December

WINTER AND SPRING are the seasons when southern gardens are at their best, and how lovely they seem to us who have fled the stark white realism of a northern winter! How delightful it is to find the sweet-leaved geraniums enduring out of doors in mid-winter, and roses blooming undiminished. Many of the shrubs are evergreen so that the gardens appear fresh and well furnished. Jasmines trail from the eves of the houses, or festoon the trees with their delicate foliage and exquisitely scented stars. Michelia figo [Magnolia fuscata], known in the North only as a greenhouse plant, lives out of doors all winter in the far South and gives to the air its exotic scent of banana. The sweet olives yield their ravishing tonic odour with a delicate reserve and the camphor tree "answers fragrantly the grasp of the hand." Myrtles are there with scented leaves and flowers, and the splendid large-flowered magnolias, pittosporums of refined fragrance, the perfumed oleanders, and the exquisite gardenia, these and many more.

1

2

3

4

5

6

7

8

9

10

11

When I discovered a new plant, I sat
down beside it for a minute or a day,
to make its acquaintance and hear
what it had to tell . . .

—JOHN MUIR

12

13

14

15

16

17

18

19

20

Poets have ever known how to turn to
gentle remedial things in times of stress,
to draw from simple sources healing
balms and assuagements. The scents of
flowers and leaves are without doubt
among the most potent sources of such
alleviation.

—L.B.W.

21

22

23

24

25

26

27

28

29

30

31

I will no longer permit the avid and eager
eye to steal away my whole attention. I
will learn to enjoy more completely all
the varied wonders of the earth.

—D. GRAYSON

NOTES